D0113887

Contents

First published 2010 by Brown Watson
The Old Mill, 76 Fleckney Road,
Kibworth Beauchamp, Leic LE8 0HG

ISBN: 978-0-7097-1904-5

My Little Book of
Christmas Carols

Illustrations by Gill Guile

Brown Watson
ENGLAND

Away in a manger

Away in a manger, no crib for a bed,
The little Lord Jesus lay down His sweet head.
The stars in the bright sky looked down where He lay,
The little Lord Jesus asleep on the hay.

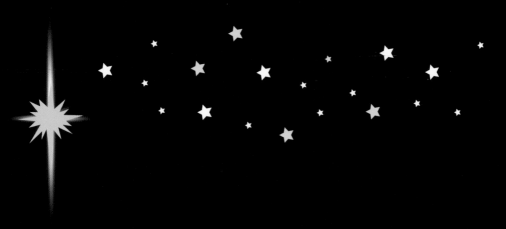

The cattle are lowing, the Baby awakes,
But little Lord Jesus, no crying He makes.
I love Thee, Lord Jesus! Look down from the sky,
And stay by my side, until morning is nigh.

Be near me, Lord Jesus, I ask Thee to stay
Close by me forever, and love me, I pray.
Bless all the dear children in Thy tender care,
And take us to heaven to live with Thee there.

Deck the hall

Deck the hall with boughs of holly,
Fa la la la la, la la la la.
'Tis the season to be jolly,
Fa la la la la la, la la la la.
Don we now our gay apparel,
Fa la la, la la la, la la la.
Sing the ancient Christmas carol,
Fa la la la la la, la la la la.

See the blazing Yule before us,
Fa la la la la, la la la la.
Strike the harp and join the chorus,
Fa la la la la, la la la la.
Follow me in merry measure,
Fa la la, la la la, la la la.
While I tell of Yuletide treasure,
Fa la la la la, la la la la.

Fast away the old year passes,
Fa la la la la, la la la la.
Hail the new, ye lads and lasses,
Fa la la la la, la la la la.
Sing we joyous, all together,
Fa la la, la la la, la la la.
Heedless of the wind and weather,
Fa la la la la, la la la la.

We three kings of Orient are

We three kings of Orient are,
Bearing gifts we traverse afar,
Field and fountain, moor and mountain,
Following yonder star.

O star of wonder, star of light,
Star with royal beauty bright,
Westward leading, still proceeding,
Guide us to thy perfect light.

Born a King on Bethlehem's plain,
Gold I bring to crown Him again,
King forever, ceasing never,
Over us all to reign.

O Star of wonder, star of light…

Frankincense to offer have I,
Incense owns a deity nigh;
Prayer and praising, voices raising,
Worshiping God on high.

O Star of wonder, star of light…

Myrrh is mine, its bitter perfume
Breathes of life of gathering gloom;
Sorrowing, sighing, bleeding, dying,
Sealed in the stone-cold tomb.

O Star of wonder, star of light…

Glorious now behold Him arise,
King and God and sacrifice,
Alleluia, Alleluia;
Sounds through the earth and skies.

O Star of wonder, star of light…

O Christmas tree

O Christmas tree! O Christmas tree!
Thy leaves are so unchanging;
O Christmas tree! O Christmas tree!
Thy leaves are so unchanging;
Not only green when summer's here,
But also when 'tis cold and drear.
O Christmas tree! O Christmas tree!
Thy leaves are so unchanging!

O Christmas tree! O Christmas tree!
Much pleasure thou can'st give me;
O Christmas tree! O Christmas tree!
Much pleasure thou can'st give me;
How often has the Christmas tree
Afforded me the greatest glee!
O Christmas tree! O Christmas tree!
Much pleasure thou can'st give me.

O Christmas tree! O Christmas tree!
Thy candles shine so brightly!
O Christmas tree! O Christmas tree!
Thy candles shine so brightly!
From base to summit, gay and bright,
There's only splendour for the sight.
O Christmas tree! O Christmas tree!
Thy candles shine so brightly!

O Christmas tree! O Christmas tree!
How richly God has decked thee!
O Christmas tree! O Christmas tree!
How richly God has decked thee!
Thou bidst us true and faithful be,
And trust in God unchangingly.
O Christmas tree! O Christmas tree!
How richly God has decked thee!

O little town of Bethlehem

O little town of Bethlehem,
How still we see thee lie!
Above thy deep and dreamless sleep
The silent stars go by:
Yet in your dark streets shining
Is everlasting Light;
The hopes and fears of all the years
Are met in thee tonight.

O morning stars, together
Proclaim the holy birth.
And praises sing to God the King,
And peace to men on Earth.
For Christ is born of Mary;
And gathered all above,
While mortals sleep, the angels keep
Their watch of wondering love.

How silently, how silently,
The wondrous gift is given!
So God imparts to human hearts
The blessings of His heaven.
No ear may hear His coming;
But in this world of sin,
Where meek souls will receive Him, still
The dear Christ enters in.

O holy Child of Bethlehem,
Descend to us, we pray;
Cast out our sin, and enter in;
Be born in us today.
We hear the Christmas angels
The great glad tidings tell;
O, come to us, abide with us,
Our Lord Emmanuel.

We wish you a merry Christmas

We wish you a merry Christmas,
We wish you a merry Christmas,
We wish you a merry Christmas,
and a happy New Year!

Good tidings we bring,
To you and your kin;
We wish you a merry Christmas,
And a happy New Year!

Oh, bring us a figgy pudding,
Oh, bring us a figgy pudding,
Oh, bring us a figgy pudding,
and a cup of good cheer!

Good tidings we bring…

We won't go until we get some,
We won't go until we get some,
We won't go until we get some,
So bring some out here!

Good tidings we bring…

Good King Wenceslas

Good King Wenceslas looked out,
On the feast of Stephen,
When the snow lay round about,
Deep and crisp and even.
Brightly shone the moon that night,
Though the frost was cruel,
When a poor man came in sight,
Gath'ring winter fuel.

"Hither, page, and stand by me,
If thou know'st it, telling,
Yonder peasant, who is he?
Where and what his dwelling?"
"Sire, he lives a good league hence,
Underneath the mountain,
Right against the forest fence,
By Saint Agnes' fountain."

"Bring me flesh and bring me wine,
Bring me pine logs hither:
Thou and I will see him dine,
When we bear him thither."
Page and monarch forth they went,
Forth they went together;
Through the rude wind's wild lament,
And the bitter weather.

"Sire, the night is darker now,
And the wind blows stronger;
Fails my heart, I know not how,
I can go no longer."
"Mark my footsteps, my good page,
Tread thou in them boldly:
Thou shalt find the winter's rage
Freeze thy blood less coldly."

In his master's steps he trod,
Where the snow lay dinted;
Heat was in the very sod
Which the Saint had printed.
Therefore, Christian men, be sure,
Wealth or rank possessing,
Ye who now will bless the poor,
Shall yourselves find blessing.

I saw three ships

I saw three ships come sailing in,
On Christmas Day, on Christmas Day,
I saw three ships come sailing in,
On Christmas Day in the morning.

And what was in those ships all three?
On Christmas Day, on Christmas Day,
And what was in those ships all three?
On Christmas Day in the morning.

The Virgin Mary and Christ were there,
On Christmas Day, on Christmas Day,
The Virgin Mary and Christ were there,
On Christmas Day in the morning.

Pray, whither sailed those ships all three?
On Christmas Day, on Christmas Day,
Pray, whither sailed those ships all three?
On Christmas Day in the morning.

O they sailed into Bethlehem,
On Christmas Day, on Christmas Day,
O they sailed into Bethlehem,
On Christmas Day in the morning.

And all the bells on earth shall ring,
On Christmas Day, on Christmas Day;
And all the bells on earth shall ring,
On Christmas Day in the morning.

And all the Angels in Heaven shall sing,
On Christmas Day, on Christmas Day,
And all the Angels in Heaven shall sing,
On Christmas Day in the morning.

And all the souls on earth shall sing,
On Christmas Day, on Christmas Day,
And all the souls on earth shall sing,
On Christmas Day in the morning.

Then let us all rejoice, amain!
On Christmas Day, on Christmas Day,
Then let us all rejoice, amain!
On Christmas Day in the morning.

While shepherds watched their flocks

While shepherds watched their flocks by night,
All seated on the ground,
The angel of the Lord came down,
And glory shone around.

"Fear not," said he, for mighty dread
Had seized their troubled mind,
"Glad tidings of great joy I bring
To you and all mankind."

"To you in David's town this day
Is born of David's line
A Saviour, who is Christ the Lord,
And this shall be the sign:

"The heavenly Babe you there shall find
To human view displayed,
All meanly wrapped in swaddling bands,
And in a manger laid."

Thus spake the seraph, and forthwith
Appeared a shining throng
Of angels praising God, who thus
Addressed their joyful song:

"All glory be to God on high,
And to the earth be peace,
Goodwill henceforth from heaven to men
Begin and never cease."

Ding dong! Merrily on high

Ding dong! Merrily on high
In heaven the bells are ringing:
Ding dong! Verily the sky
Is riven with Angels singing.

Gloria, Hosanna in excelsis!
Gloria, Hosanna in excelsis!

E'en so, here below, below
Let steeple bells be swungen;
And i-o, i-o, i-o,
By priest and people sungen.

Gloria, Hosanna in excelsis!
Gloria, Hosanna in excelsis!

Pray you, dutifully prime
Your matin chime, ye ringers;
May you beautifully rime
Your eve-time song, ye singers

Gloria, Hosanna in excelsis!
Gloria, Hosanna in excelsis!

Silent night

Silent night, holy night,
All is calm, all is bright.
Round yon Virgin Mother and Child,
Holy Infant so tender and mild.
Sleep in heavenly peace,
Sleep in heavenly peace.

Silent night, holy night,
Shepherds quake at the sight.
Glories stream from heaven afar,
Heavenly hosts sing Alleluia.
Christ, the Saviour is born,
Christ, the Saviour is born.

Silent night, holy night,
Son of God, love's pure light.
Radiant beams from Thy holy face,
With the dawn of redeeming grace,
Jesus, Lord, at Thy birth,
Jesus, Lord, at Thy birth.

Jingle bells

Dashing through the snow,
In a one horse open sleigh,
O'er the fields we go,
Laughing all the way.
Bells on bob tails ring,
Making spirits bright,
What fun it is to laugh and sing
A sleighing song tonight!

Oh, jingle bells, jingle bells,
Jingle all the way.
Oh, what fun it is to ride
In a one horse open sleigh!
Jingle bells, jingle bells,
Jingle all the way.
Oh, what fun it is to ride
In a one horse open sleigh!

A day or two ago,
I thought I'd take a ride
And soon Miss Fanny Bright
Was seated by my side.
The horse was lean and lank,
Misfortune seemed his lot,
We got into a drifted bank
And then we got upsot!

Oh, jingle bells, jingle bells,
Jingle all the way.
Oh, what fun it is to ride
In a one horse open sleigh!
Oh, jingle bells, jingle bells,
Jingle all the way.
Oh, what fun it is to ride
In a one horse open sleigh yeah!